level 2

TECHNIC LESSONS

by JAMES BASTIEN

KJOS WEST · Neil A. Kjos, Jr. Publisher · San Diego, California

TO THE TEACHER

TECHNIC LESSONS, Level 2, is designed to be used simultaneously with **PIANO LESSONS, Level 2** (©*1976 KJOS WEST, San Diego, California, Ed. No. WP3*). It may also be used with any piano course.

DYNAMICS — Unless indicated, the dynamics are to be suggested by the teacher. On each repeat of the exercise, have the student use a different dynamic level.

TEMPO — Direct the student to play each exercise in three tempos: slow, medium and fast. On each repeat, have the student use a different tempo.

TOUCH — Some exercises have specific directions to practice both legato and staccato. Many of the legato exercises (those with slurs) may also be played staccato at the teacher's discretion.

TRANSPOSITION — Transposition is indicated for some exercises. Additional transposition for these exercises may be suggested at the teacher's discretion.

The goal of **TECHNIC LESSONS** is to develop hand and finger coordination and facility, and to develop ease and control at the keyboard. A variety of keyboard experiences is provided to give the student a basic foundation in beginning fundamentals.

Suggested Use of Materials with "PIANO LESSONS, Level 2."

After completing **page 5,** the student is ready to begin . . . . **Theory Lessons**-Level 2 (WP8)
After completing **page 7,** the student is ready to begin . . . . **Technic Lessons**-Level 2 (WP13)
After completing **page 13,** the student is ready to begin . . . . **Piano Solos**-Level 2 (WP24)
After completing **page 15,** the student is ready to begin . . . . **Sight Reading**-Level 2 (WP17)
After completing **page 18,** the student is ready to begin
   these Supplementary Books . . . . **Bastien Favorites**-Level 2 (GP84)
                                               Duet Favorites-Level 2 (WP61)
                                              Christmas Favorites-Level 2 (WP50)
                                              Christmas Duets-Level 2 (GP312)
                                         Favorite Classic Melodies-Level 2 (WP74)
                                             Hymn Favorites-Level 2 (WP45)
                                            Piano Recital Solos-Level 2 (WP66)
                                           Pop Piano Styles-Level 2 (WP52)

SHEET MUSIC from **Level Two Solos** may be assigned to the student at the teacher's discretion.

8/81

ISBN 0-8497-5012-1

TO THE STUDENT

The studies in this book are designed to help you play the piano with ease and control. Allow time each day for technic practice. You might use these studies as warm-ups before beginning to practice your pieces.

Think of these three points often.

HEIGHT Sit up high enough to reach the keys easily. Your wrists and forearms should be in a *straight line* over the keys. Do you have a piano stool or a piano chair at home which moves up and down? If not, cushions or telephone books will help raise you up when you practice.

POSTURE Sit up *straight* in front of the center of the piano. Place your feet flat on the floor.

HAND POSITION When playing the piano, hold your fingers in a nice *curved shape*. Imagine you are holding a ball. This is the way the fingers should be curved when playing the piano.

CONTENTS

FIVE FINGER PATTERNS

WALKING~RUNNING

1st time—*legato*
2nd time—*staccato*

© **1976 Kjos West, San Diego, California**
Inter. Copyright Secured   All Rights Reserved   Printed in U.S.A.

MARCH OF THE MARTIANS

DIZZY FINGERS

DOTTED RHYTHM STUDIES

1.

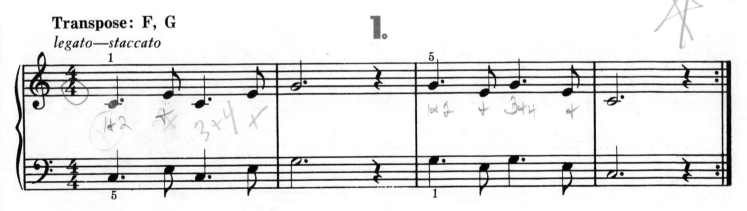

2.

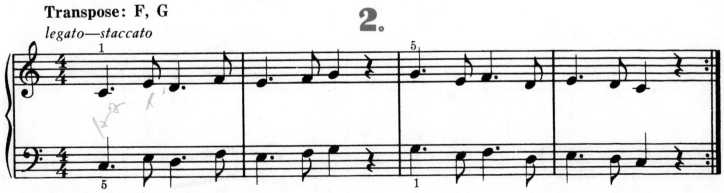

C MAJOR SCALE STUDIES

1.

2.

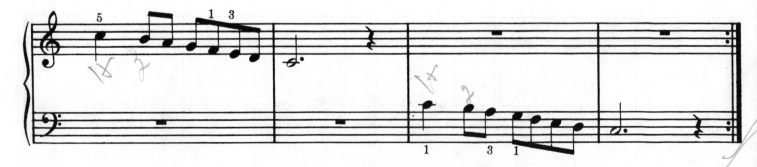

3.

Contrary Motion

4.

Contrary Motion

5.

Contrary Motion

6.

Parallel Motion

8

5THS~6THS

STRETCHING

FOLLOW THE LEADER

SNOW GLISTENING

I V₇ CHORDS IN C MAJOR

WARM-UPS

RED ROCKET

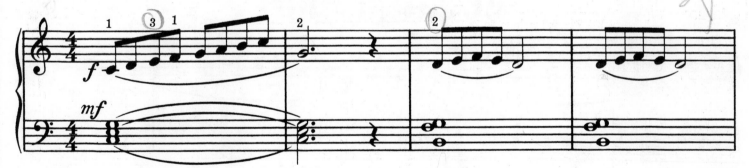

PRIMARY CHORDS IN C MAJOR

LIFTING WEIGHTS

ROCKING HIGH

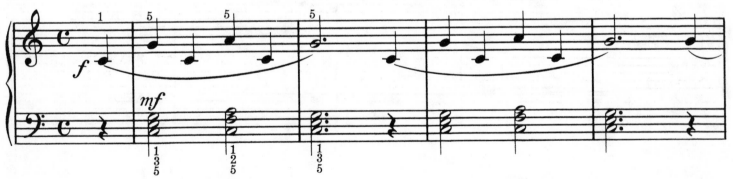

ROCKING LOW

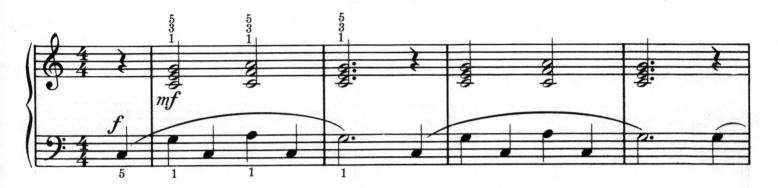

LAUGH WITH ME

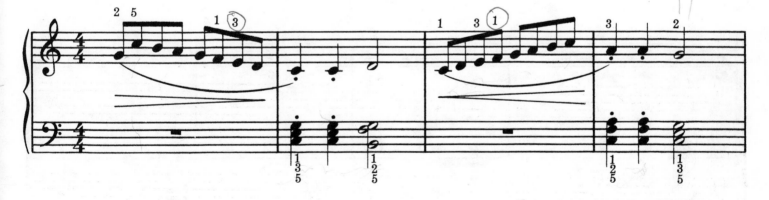

WP 13

Phrase = Musical Sentence

PHRASING STUDIES

1.

Oct. 2

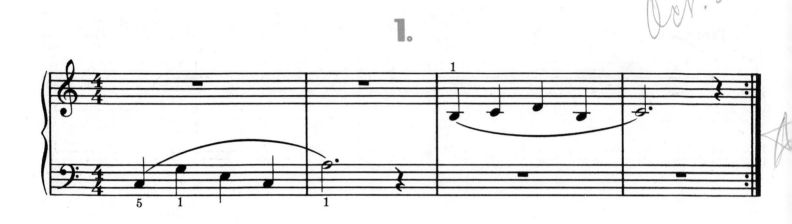

2.

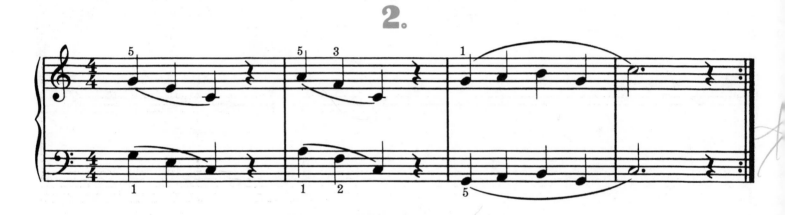

3.

4.

Oct. 9

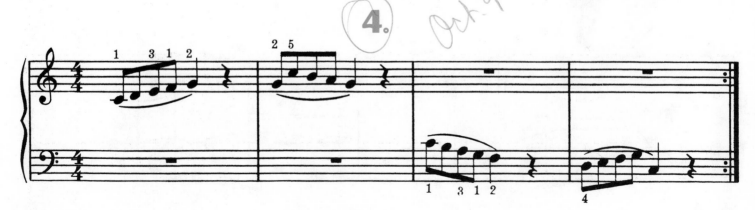

LEGATO~STACCATO STUDIES

STEP, HOP 1.

Transpose: F, G

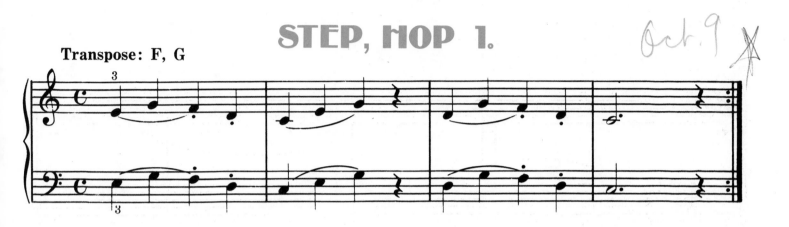

STEP, HOP 2.

HOP, GLIDE

G MAJOR SCALE STUDIES

1.

legato—staccato

2.

Contrary Motion

3.

Parallel Motion

I V₇ CHORDS IN G MAJOR

WARM~UPS

AIRPLANE RIDE

PRIMARY CHORDS IN G MAJOR

WARM-UPS

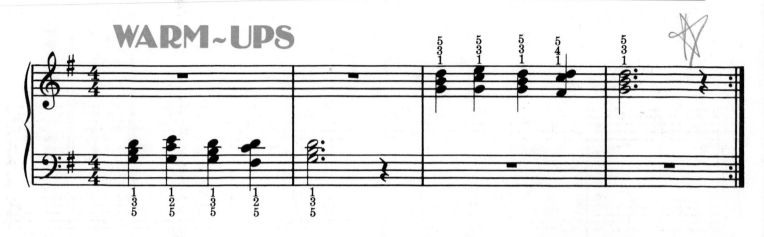

MARCHING~RIGHT FOOT

MARCHING~LEFT FOOT

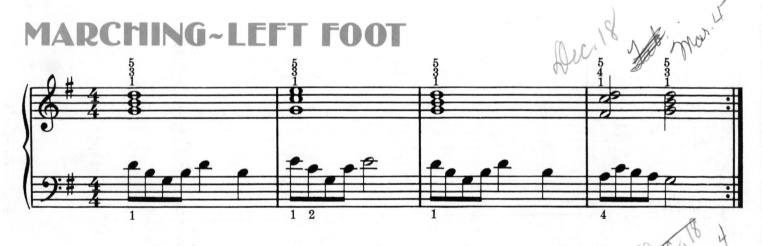

WHISTLING A TUNE

$\frac{6}{8}$ RHYTHM STUDIES

Transpose: F, C

1.

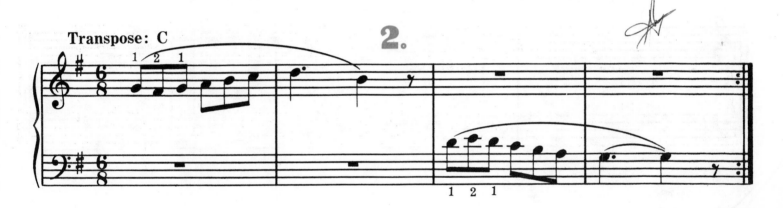

Transpose: C

2.

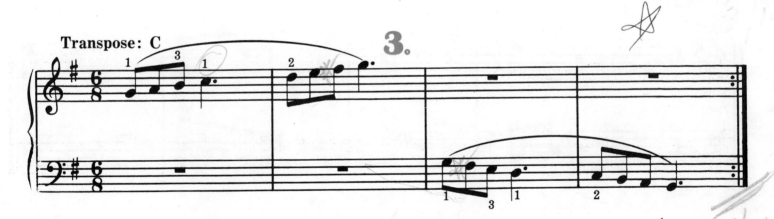

Transpose: C

3.

BUNNY HOP

Transpose: C

F MAJOR SCALE STUDIES

1.

legato—staccato

2.

Contrary Motion

3.

Parallel Motion

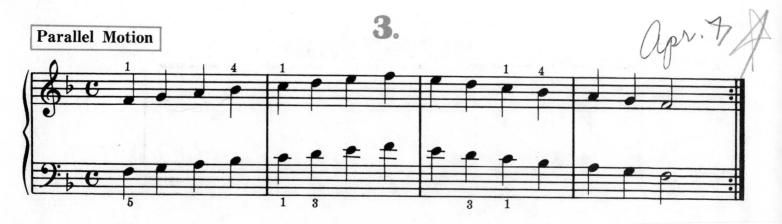

PRIMARY CHORDS IN F MAJOR

WARM-UPS

JUMPING

ON TIPTOE

TWIN ENGINES

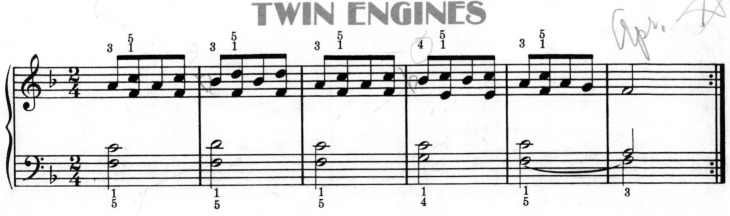

WP13

SCALE ETUDES

1.

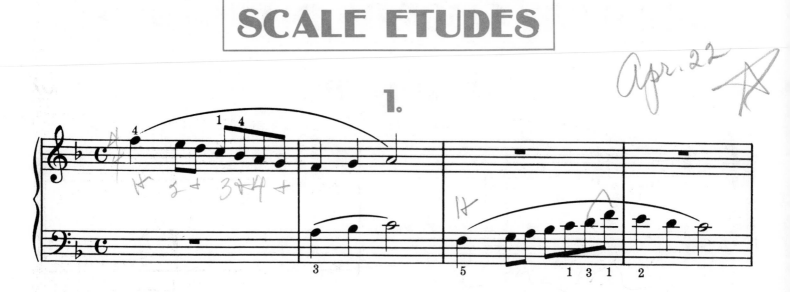

2.

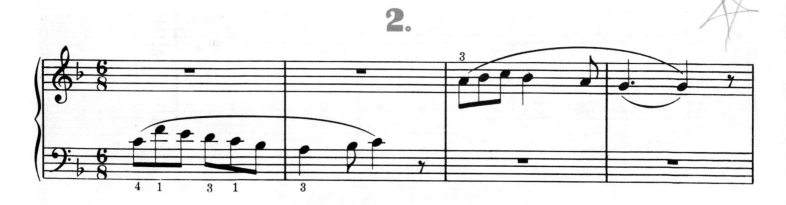

VARIED STUDIES

ICE-SKATING

FIDDLE-FADDLE 1.

Transpose: F, G
legato—staccato

FIDDLE-FADDLE 2.

NEAT TRICK

Hold thumbs down throughout.

D MAJOR SCALE STUDIES

1.

legato—staccato

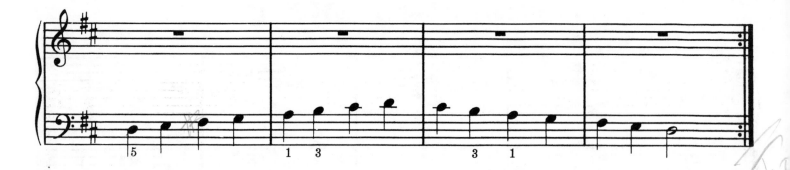

Contrary Motion

2.

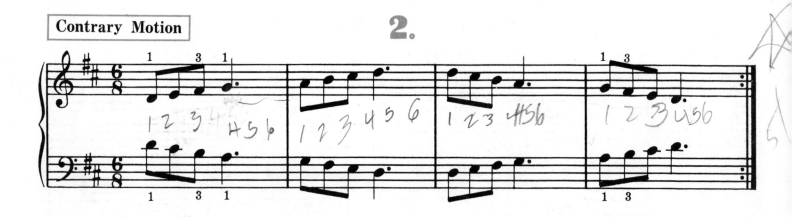

Parallel Motion

3.

PRIMARY CHORDS IN D MAJOR

WARM-UPS

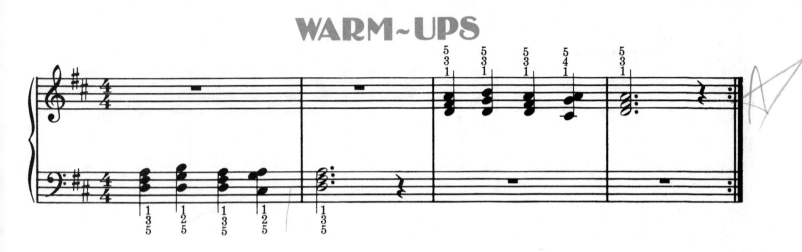

TURNABOUT

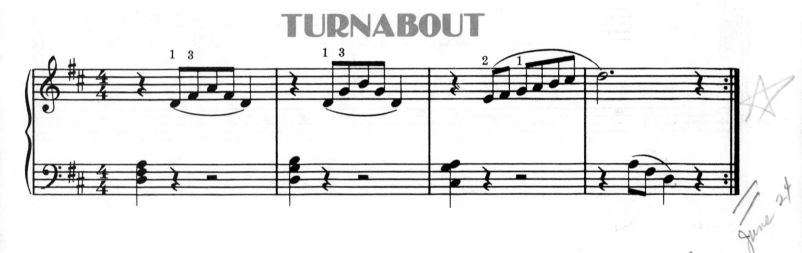

ICE-SKATING

A MAJOR SCALE STUDIES

1.

legato—staccato

2.

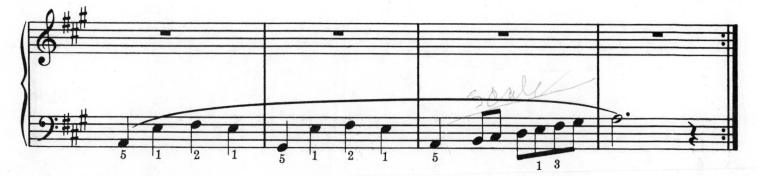

PRIMARY CHORDS IN A MAJOR

WARM~UPS

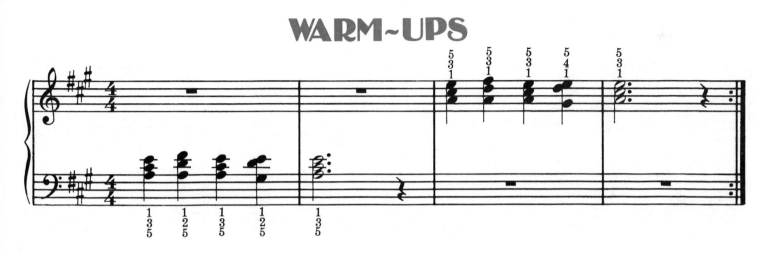

SONG AT DUSK

ROLLING HOOPS

E MAJOR SCALE STUDIES

1.

legato—staccato

2.

PRIMARY CHORDS IN E MAJOR

WARM-UPS

STRICTLY STACCATO

THE SPLITS

ROCK ALONG

MINOR CHORDS

SLOW CRAWL

RUNNING ALONG

GOING HOME

CROSSING HANDS

HILL CLIMB

CHROMATICS

ANT CRAWLING

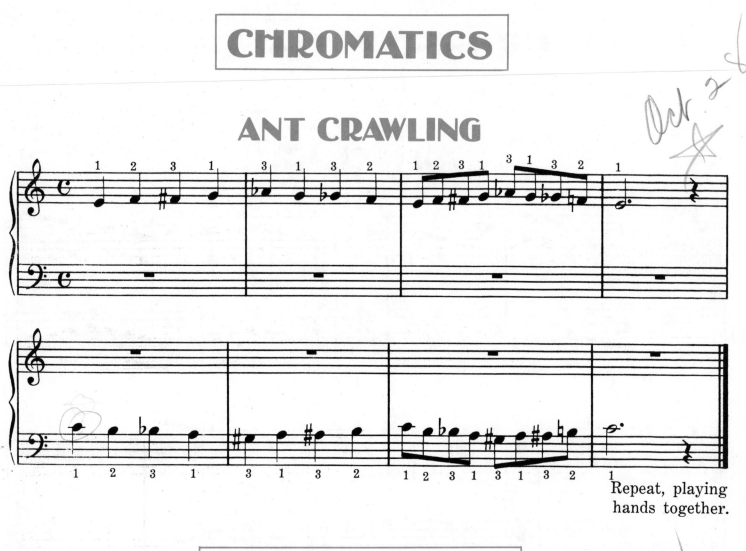

Repeat, playing hands together.

DOUBLE NOTES

TWO~STEP

Repeat, playing hands together.

WP13

FINGER EXTENSION STUDY

MISTER HANON

legato—staccato

going up

coming down

TEACHER'S TECHNIC